MATHEMATICS ACCOMPLISHED

Y4 BOOSTER

TEACHING ASSISTANT'S BOOK

Stefanie Sullivan

Acknowledgements

Our thanks to Jackie Trudgeon and Sheila Viegas, Year 6 teachers from Tower Hamlets, London, who provided the inspiration for this book.

Thanks also to the BEAM Development Group:
Jo Barratt, Rotherfield Primary School, Islington
Mark Day, Hanover Primary School, Islington
Catherine Horton, St Jude and St Paul's Primary School, Islington
Simone de Juan, Prior Weston Primary School, Islington
Helen Wood, Vittoria Primary School, Islington

Published by BEAM Education
Maze Workshops
72a Southgate Road
London N1 3JT
Telephone 020 7684 3323
Fax 020 7684 3334
Email info@beam.co.uk
www.beam.co.uk
© BEAM Education 2007, a division of Nelson Thornes
ISBN 978 1 906224 20 2
British Library Cataloguing-in-Publication Data
Data available
Edited by Marion Dill
Cover design by Malena Wilson-Max
Layout by Suzan Aral, Reena Kataria and Matt Carr
Printed in Spain

Contents

Introduction

HOW TO USE THIS BOOK

The *Year 4 Booster* Teacher's book contains 30 lessons for a teacher to use with a group of children. This can be the whole class or a selected group. Each lesson focuses on a specific skill or idea that children often find difficult.

Each of the 30 teacher's lessons has a follow-up activity to go with it. These follow-up activities are detailed in this Teaching assistant's book, and they are intended for you to use with a selected group of children who need more practice.

The sessions are all presented on a double page like this.

Vocabulary

This is a list of key words and phrases that children need to learn, understand and use when talking about their work. Try to use these words yourself when you talk with children, in a context that shows what they mean – then the words will become familiar and meaningful to children..

Activity

This is what you actually do with the children. It may be a game, an activity or working through an activity sheet.

We have included examples of questions or prompts for you to present to children. This will help challenge their mathematical thinking further and encourage children to discuss mathematical processes.

About the maths

In this section, you will find information about the way children learn maths as well as answers to any maths questions on the resource sheets. We will also indicate misconceptions the children may have.

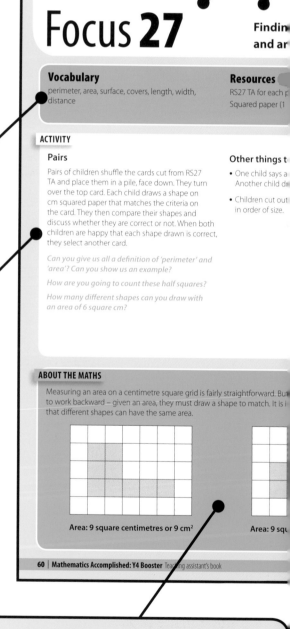

Focus 27

Findin
and ar

Vocabulary
perimeter, area, surface, covers, length, width, distance

Resources
RS27 TA for each p
Squared paper (1

ACTIVITY

Pairs

Pairs of children shuffle the cards cut from RS27 TA and place them in a pile, face down. They turn over the top card. Each child draws a shape on cm squared paper that matches the criteria on the card. They then compare their shapes and discuss whether they are correct or not. When both children are happy that each shape drawn is correct, they select another card.

Can you give us all a definition of 'perimeter' and 'area'? Can you show us an example?

How are you going to count these half squares?

How many different shapes can you draw with an area of 6 square cm?

Other things t
• One child says a
  Another child d
• Children cut ou
  in order of size.

ABOUT THE MATHS

Measuring an area on a centimetre square grid is fairly straightforward. But
to work backward – given an area, they must draw a shape to match. It is i
that different shapes can have the same area.

Area: 9 square centimetres or 9 cm²   Area: 9 squ

Focus and learning objective

The Focus number tells you which session in the Teacher's book this activity follows up. The learning objective indicates what children will learn from the activity.

Resources

This is a list of the materials to prepare before your session with the children. There is always a photocopiable resource sheet in the list, which is provided on the opposite page. We presume you always have pencils and paper to hand, so they are not listed here.

RS**27** TA

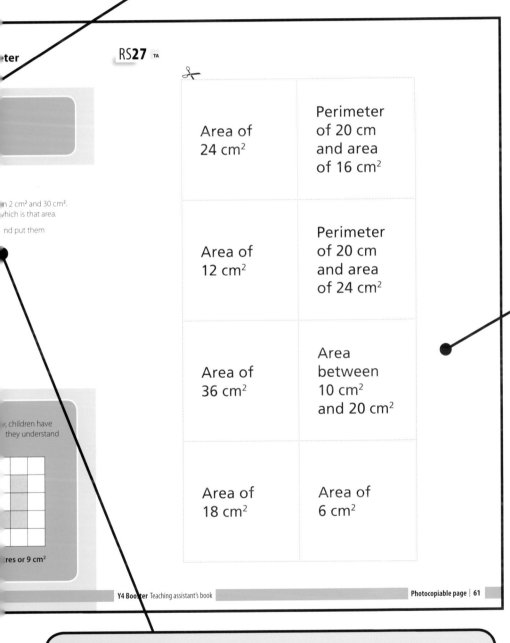

Area of 24 cm²	Perimeter of 20 cm and area of 16 cm²
Area of 12 cm²	Perimeter of 20 cm and area of 24 cm²
Area of 36 cm²	Area between 10 cm² and 20 cm²
Area of 18 cm²	Area of 6 cm²

n 2 cm² and 30 cm².
vhich is that area.

nd put them

, children have
they understand

res or 9 cm²

Resource sheet

Each session comes with a resource sheet. You give this sheet to the children as it is, you cut it up into cards or slips of paper, or you use the sheet to play a game with. The instructions are always in the 'Activity' section on the opposite page.

There are 10 further resource sheets at the back of the book. These contain materials you may need in two or more activities: number lines, number cards, spinners, and so on.

Other things to do

Sometimes there are simpler or different versions of the main activity. Sometimes there are ideas for children who have finished an activity.

Focus 1

Solving one- and two-step money problems

Vocabulary

word problem, method, information, solve, answer, money, coin, note, buy, spend, cost, pence, pound, how much?, how many?

Resources

Cards cut from RS1 TA for each pair

ACTIVITY

Pairs

Pairs of children shuffle the cards and place them on the table, face down. They turn over the top card and place it on the table. Each child then writes a word problem that matches the criteria on the card.

Discuss with the children the problems they created and whether they matched the criteria or not.

Can you give me an example of a 'mathematical operation'?

What if you had to use division instead of multiplication? How would you change the problem?

Should I do the addition or the multiplication first? Or doesn't it matter?

Other things to do

- Help children make up simple sums that fit the criteria on the card, then use these as a basis for their word problem. For example, $130 - 6 = 124$ becomes "I saved £130, and I spent £6. How much did I have left?"

- Help children use a calculator to check their calculations. This will involve thinking about how to key in amounts of money and interpret the display, even though there is no pound sign (£) on the calculator.

ABOUT THE MATHS

In the teacher's lesson, children worked on solving money problems. In this session, they need to make up problems with a given answer, using mathematical operations (calculations). These can be as simple or complex as the children choose.

For example:

Answer: £124

Solve, using subtraction only.

A child might write: "I had £200, and I lost £76. How much did I have left?"

Problems with two operations will need to be more complex. For example:

Answer: £32

Solve, using multiplication and subtraction.

A child might write: "I earn £10 every time I help my uncle on his stall. I helped him 4 times, then I bought a game for £8. How much money did I have then?"

Answer: **£124** Solve, using subtraction only.	Answer: **£240** Solve, using multiplication only.
Answer: **13p** Solve, using division only.	Answer: **£786** Solve, using addition only.
Answer: **£2.60** Solve, using two mathematical operations.	Answer: **£8.80** Solve, using multiplication and addition.
Answer: **£32** Solve, using multiplication and subtraction.	Answer: **42p** Solve, using subtraction only.
Answer: **72p** Solve, using multiplication only.	Answer: **£5.40** Solve, using two mathematical operations.

Focus 2

Vocabulary

word problem, method, information, solve, answer, centimetres, miles, litres, millilitres, kilograms, grams

Resources

RS2 TA for each child
Individual wipe boards

ACTIVITY

Whole group

Children work with a set of problem cards cut from RS2 TA and individual wipe boards. They shuffle the cards and place them in a pile on the table, face down. They turn over the top card and display it for all to see, then look at it in silence and write down on their boards what operation they would use to solve it.

On a count of three, children show their boards. They discuss their ideas and agree as a group on the best operation for solving the problem.

Children repeat this for each card until they are sorted into four piles: $+$, $-$, $\times$, $\div$.

If you multiply those two numbers, will you get a larger or a smaller answer?

Is there any other way you could do the calculation?

Can you explain how you know what calculation to do?

Other things to do

- Once children have worked out whether a problem is $+$, $-$, $\times$ or $\div$, help them use a calculator to find the answer to the problem. This will involve thinking about how to key in measures and interpret the display, even though there are no weights and measures signs (kg, ml, cm, and so on) on the calculator.

- Children make up problems for each other to solve – or for you to solve!

ABOUT THE MATHS

Children are not being asked to calculate the answers to these problems, just to say how to solve them. This takes off the pressure and allows them to concentrate on what the problem means and to think about whether it involves addition, subtraction, multiplication or division.

Luke needs 18 pieces of string.

Each one needs to be 15 cm long.

How much string does he need in total?

A lift is carrying three people whose weights are 64 kg, 78 kg and 59 kg.

What is the total weight the lift is carrying?

Four cars fill up at a petrol pump.

The first gets 28 l, the second 47 l, the third 16 l and the fourth 52 l.

How much petrol has gone from the pump?

How many 5 cm pieces can you cut from a piece of string 145 cm long?

Mr Roberts is 174 cm tall, and his son, Harry, is 137 cm tall.
What is the difference in their heights?

The Kumar family are going on holiday.

It is 437 kilometres to their hotel.

After 278 kilometres, how much further is it to go?

A tablespoon holds 15 ml of vinegar.

A bottle holds 20 tablespoons.

How many millilitres does the bottle hold?

A bottle holds 1800 ml of diluted squash.

How many cups holding 90 ml can be made from the bottle?

One vase holds 1750 ml of water.

Another holds 2400 ml.

How much more water does the second vase hold?

A baker needs 75 g of butter to make a cake.

He wants to make 24 cakes.

How much butter does he need?

Three shire horses are pulling loads of wood. There are 1260 kg of wood to move.

If each horse pulled the same weight, how heavy would its load be?

At a summer fair, the first-prize marrow weighed 456 g. The second-prize marrow weighed 368 g.

How much heavier was the winning marrow?

Focus 3

Ordering and rounding four-digit whole numbers

ACTIVITY

Pairs

Pairs of children work with a copy of RS3 TA each. They take it in turns to roll the dice four times and record the digits. Without looking at their partner's work, each child uses the digits to make the smallest number and the largest number they can. They then round the numbers to the nearest 10, 100 and 1000.

When they have finished, they show each other their answers. If the answers are not the same, both children discuss their thoughts and agree on the correct answer.

This activity can be repeated as many times as required. Instead of using the resource sheet, the table could be drawn onto individual wipe boards for children to write on and show each other.

Can you think of a situation when it is useful to round a number up or down?

What number might have been rounded up to 3000? Or rounded down to 220?

Have any different numbers rounded to the same number? Why is that?

Other things to do

- Start off with three-digit numbers (roll the dice three times). Then move on to four-digit numbers when children are ready.

- Help children draw number lines and put their number on the line, along with whatever other numbers they find helpful. Then work out whether the number rounds down or up.

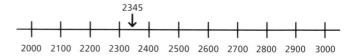

2345 must round down to 2000.

ABOUT THE MATHS

Children need to focus on the relevant digit when they are rounding. For example:

2479

Round to the nearest 1000? Look at the hundreds digit. 2<u>4</u>79 rounds <u>down</u> to 2000.

Round to the nearest 100? Look at the tens digit. 24<u>7</u>9 rounds <u>up</u> to 2500.

Round to the nearest 10? Look at the ones digit. 247<u>9</u> rounds <u>up</u> to 2480.

The digits rolled are: ☐ ☐ ☐ ☐

	Smallest number	Largest number
Rounded to the nearest 1000		
Rounded to the nearest 100		
Rounded to the nearest 10		

The digits rolled are: ☐ ☐ ☐ ☐

	Smallest number	Largest number
Rounded to the nearest 1000		
Rounded to the nearest 100		
Rounded to the nearest 10		

The digits rolled are: ☐ ☐ ☐ ☐

	Smallest number	Largest number
Rounded to the nearest 1000		
Rounded to the nearest 100		
Rounded to the nearest 10		

Focus 4

Vocabulary

positive, negative, above zero, below zero, minus

Resources

Set of −15 to 15 number cards cut from RS4 TA for each pair

ACTIVITY

Pairs

Children share a cut-up copy of RS4 TA. They remove 0 and place it in the centre of the table, face up. They shuffle the remaining cards and lay 15 cards in a line face down each side of zero. Child A picks up a card from the line, turns it face up and decides the correct place to put it in the line.

They pick up the card already in that place and give it to Child B, who replaces it in the line with the card they are holding. Child B decides the correct position for the card they have been given, picks up the card already in that place, gives it to Child A and replaces it in the line with the card they are holding.

The children continue like this until they are unable to pick up a card or they have turned over all the cards.

What numbers are before − 2?

Can you tell me the numbers either side of − 8?

Can you count backward from 4 to − 4?

Other things to do

- One child picks a number card and circles that number on a number line. Their partner picks another number and circles it in a different colour. They keep taking turns until one of them has 5 consecutive numbers circled in their colour.

- Children draw their own number line from 0 to −30.

ABOUT THE MATHS

This game is very similar to 'Clock patience' and gives the chidren practice in constructing a negative number line.

You can observe how confident children are with using a negative number line when, during the game, children are deciding where to place their cards. Those who are fairly secure with the order of the numbers will count backward or forward from the nearest negative card showing, whereas children who are less secure will count back from zero.

−8	0	8	
−9	−1	7	15
−10	−2	6	14
−11	−3	5	13
−12	−4	4	12
−13	−5	3	11
−14	−6	2	10
−15	−7	1	9

Focus 5

Using inequalities

Vocabulary

greater than, less than, <, >, compare

Resources

RS5 TA for each pair

Set of −20 to 20 number cards for each pair

ACTIVITY

Pairs

Cut RS5 TA in half and give each child a chart.

Shuffle the set of number cards and place them on the table, face down. Children take it in turns to turn over two cards. Both children enter the two numbers on their chart, starting at the top and working their way down, to create a true statement. When they are ready, they say 'Show me' and show each other what they have written.

They then compare the two answers and check that both statements are true: if this is the case, the numbers should be in the opposite positions on each chart.

Can you show where these two numbers are on the number line?

Can you explain to your partner why −6 is less than 3?

Can you think of a situation where it is important to know which number is greater?

Other things to do

• Sketch a large < and > on paper and place number cards either side of one of the signs to make true or false statements. You can make easy or more difficult statements.

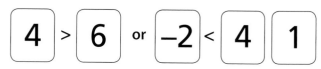

Children have to say whether your statement is correct or not.

• Both children read out their statements (which gives them practice in speaking the < and > symbols).

Child A: *3 is greater than −2.*

Child B: *−2 is less than 3.*

ABOUT THE MATHS

By this age, children are familiar with writing equations using the = symbol.

$3 + 21 = 24$ $5 \times 9 = 45$ **and so on**

But now they are learning to use the symbols < (less than) and > (greater than).

$3 < 7$ $12 > -4$

There is no particular skill involved, simply practice in remembering which symbol means which. If children need help remembering, remind them that the small, closed end of the shape belongs with the smaller number, and the large, open end with the larger number.

$3 > 1$

Name _____

Name _____

>

>

<

>

<

>

<

<

>

<

<

>

<

>

<

>

>

<

Focus 6

Vocabulary

units, ones, tens, tenths, hundredths, place, place value, partition

Resources

RS6 TA for each child

0–9 dice for each pair

ACTIVITY

Pairs

Each child has their own copy of RS6 TA. The pair takes turns to roll the dice, twice each. Each child chooses how to arrange the digits in the four place value columns and writes the complete number in the box alongside.

For example:

My number is

T	U	.	tenths	hundredths	
3	5	.	0	9	35.09

When both children have written their number, they each say their number aloud and show each other how they made it: "Thirty-five point zero nine."

What is the correct way of saying 30.59? What is an incorrect way of saying it?

Can anyone explain how we read decimal numbers with the 0 in different places? How about 30.59, 35.09?

Who can explain when we don't write the zero?

Other things to do

- Use a 1–6 dice to keep the numbers simple (no zeros).

- Children roll the dice four times to get four digits. They arrange those four digits and a decimal point in as many different ways as they can and read out all the numbers they make.

  6 1 7 2 .

  617.2   61.72   72.16   71.62   7.126 and so on

ABOUT THE MATHS

This activity practises making and saying decimal numbers to two places. Children need to know that the two columns to the right of the decimal point represent tenths and hundredths respectively, but at this stage they do not need to be able to calculate with these numbers – or even to order them.

The convention is to say 'thirty point five nine'. It is incorrect to say 'thirty point fifty nine'. The zero is not used in the largest or the smallest columns. We don't write 03.59 or 35.90 (except with money!).

My number is										

T	U	• tenths	hundredths

Focus 7

Ordering decimals

Vocabulary

units, tenths, hundredths, place value, position, larger, smaller, between

Resources

RS7 TA for each child

ACTIVITY

Whole group and pairs

Read through RS7 TA with the children, making sure that they understand it. The sheet is a record of how much water a cycling team drank. Explain that the rectangles on the sheet represent bottles, and the task is to mark the correct water level on each rectangle.

Make sure that the children are clear that they have to show the amount of water left in the bottle.

When they have finished, children compare their sheet with a partner's and discuss any discrepancies in their answers. The aim is to agree on the correct answer. Finally, they answer the questions at the bottom of the sheet.

Would it help to put in the mark for 0.5 litres?

Can you judge about a third of the way up? What decimal is about a third of a litre?

Can you explain how to estimate where 0.86 litres is? What did you decide to do about the point nought six?

Other things to do

- Help children sketch a rectangle (to represent a 1-litre water bottle) and mark on it the 'easy' decimals to one place: 0.1 litres, 0.2 litres, 0.3 litres, 0.4 litres, 0.5 litres, 0.6 litres, 0.7 litres, 0.8 litres, 0.9 litres. They can refer to this when filling in the worksheet.

- Suggest children locate the 'bottles' where the amount of water left is a decimal to one place and complete these questions first: for example, Anna's 0.4 litres and Harry's 0.3 litres.

ABOUT THE MATHS

It is not difficult to find where, for example, 0.3 litres belongs on a 'water bottle'. Children may work out 'halfway', which is 0.5, then go down a bit.

Decimals to two places, such as 0.28 litres, are trickier. Remind children to look at the tenths digit (0.28), which tells them that the number is more than 0.2, but not as much as 0.3. The hundredths digit (0.28) tells them that the number is closer to 0.3 than to 0.2.

George left 0.35 litres.   Beth left 0.75 litres.   Merrin left 0.05 litres.   Anna left 0.4 litres.

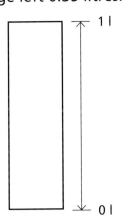 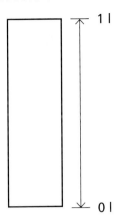 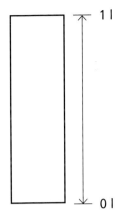 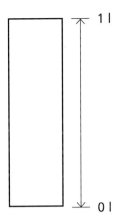

Umer left 0.6 litres.   Danny left 0.28 litres.   Saira left 0.60 litres.   Rajan left 0.90 litres.

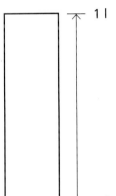 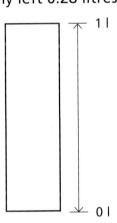 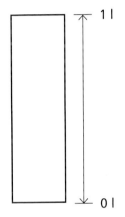 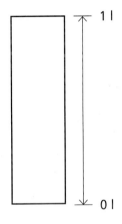

Harry left 0.3 litres.   Ali left 0.86 litres.   Joel left 0.55 litres.

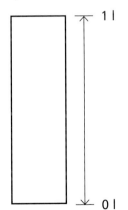 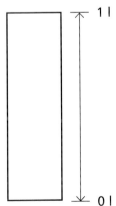 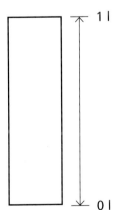

Who drank the most?

Who drank the least?

Order the team from who drank the least
to who drank the most.

FOCUS 8

Relating decimals to fractions

ACTIVITY

Pairs

Children work with a set of dominoes made from RS8 TA. They make a chain where touching dominoes match each other.

0.9	$\frac{7}{10}$	seven tenths	$\frac{1}{2}$	0.5	0.6

Which are the easiest pairs to slot together?

Which is the same as four tenths? 0.4 or 0.04? Why?

How can you read that decimal number?

Other things to do

- The chain can be closed into a loop. See if children can move the dominoes around to close the chain in this way.

- Children make two extra dominoes that can be fitted in between two existing dominoes. They will need to make sure the ends match.

0.9	$\frac{7}{10}$		0.7	0.1		$\frac{1}{10}$	$\frac{7}{10}$		seven tenths	$\frac{1}{2}$

ABOUT THE MATHS

To complete their domino chain, children need to work out the equivalence between fractions and decimals, written either in words or as symbols. They should pay attention to the differences between tenths ($\frac{4}{10}$ and 0.4) and hundredths ($\frac{4}{100}$ and 0.04).

$$0.4 = \frac{4}{10} \qquad\qquad 0.8 = \frac{8}{10} \qquad\qquad 0.04 = \frac{4}{100}$$

$$0.5 = \frac{5}{10} = \frac{1}{2} \qquad\qquad 0.9 = \frac{9}{10} \qquad\qquad 0.08 = \frac{8}{100}$$

$$0.6 = \frac{6}{10} \qquad\qquad 0.7 = \frac{7}{10}$$

$\dfrac{1}{2}$	seven tenths
zero point nine	$\dfrac{9}{100}$
0.08	$\dfrac{9}{10}$

$\dfrac{7}{10}$	0.9
0.09	$\dfrac{4}{100}$
one half	nine tenths

0.6	0.5
0.4	0.04
$\dfrac{8}{100}$	$\dfrac{5}{10}$

Focus 9

Finding equivalent fractions

Vocabulary

fraction, one whole, half, quarter, third, sixth, fifth, eighth, tenth, equivalence

Resources

Set of cards cut from RS9 TA for each child

ACTIVITY

Pairs

Children cut out the cards from RS9 TA, then sort them into fractions that are equivalent to each other, and matching diagrams.

For example:

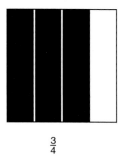

$\frac{3}{4}$

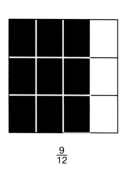

$\frac{9}{12}$

How many fractions and diagrams can you find that show a half in different ways?

How else could you shade a square to show a half?

How did you work out that the diagram shows nine twelfths?

Other things to do

- Pairs can play Pelmanism with the cards. Spread them out, face down. Children take turns to turn over two cards and say the fractions (whether it is a number or a diagram). If they match, the child keeps that pair. They keep playing until one player has 3 or 4 pairs.

- Children add some cards to one of the fraction sets: for example, another fraction worth the same as $\frac{1}{2}$ or a diagram showing $\frac{3}{4}$.

ABOUT THE MATHS

There are six sets of cards on the sheet:

- $\frac{1}{4}$ $\frac{2}{8}$ and two diagram cards to match
- $\frac{1}{3}$ $\frac{3}{9}$ and two diagram cards to match
- $\frac{2}{3}$ $\frac{4}{6}$ and two diagram cards to match

- $\frac{2}{5}$ $\frac{4}{10}$ and two diagram cards to match
- $\frac{3}{4}$ $\frac{9}{12}$ and two diagram cards to match
- $\frac{1}{2}$ $\frac{3}{6}$ $\frac{4}{8}$ $\frac{9}{12}$ and four diagram cards to match

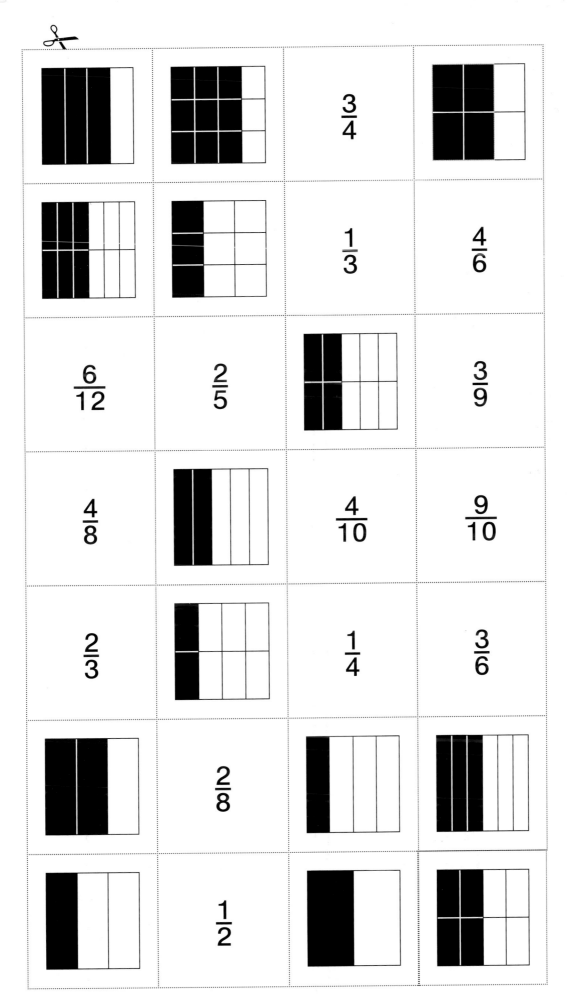

Focus 10

Using ratio and proportion

Vocabulary

in every, for every, to every, proportion, ratio, third, two thirds, whole

Resources

Set of cards cut from RS10 TA for each child

ACTIVITY

Whole group

Children work with a set of necklace cards (including two blanks) and a set of ratio and proportion cards. They spread out the cards on the table, face up.

Children then match the ratio cards to the necklaces. Where there are incomplete statements, they complete the cards. Where there is no match, they draw their own necklace card and match it to the set of cards.

How can you describe the repeating pattern?

I want to buy some triangle beads and some star beads. Do I get more triangles or more stars?

If I use 10 star beads for this necklace, how many triangle beads will I need? How do you know?

Other things to do

• Children can lay out beads in a line, or use stickers, and make a matching statement. For example:

For every two round beads there is one cube bead.

• Pick a necklace card and a statement card and put them side by side. Challenge children to say whether they match.

ABOUT THE MATHS

When children begin to learn about ratio and proportion, the phrases 'for every', 'in every' and 'to every' provide important meaning and information. For example, the following statements describe this necklace.

For every two triangles there is one star.

In every three beads there are two triangles.

There are two triangles to every star.

My necklace looks like this:

My necklace looks like this:

For every two triangles there is one star.	In every three beads there are two triangles.	There are two triangles to every star.
For every two triangles there are three stars.	In every five beads there are two triangles.	There are two triangles to every three stars.
For every four triangles there is one star.	In every five beads there is one star.	_____ to every _____ _____
For every three triangles there is one star.	In every _____ _____ _____	There are three triangles to every star.
In every five beads there are two stars.	There are three triangles to every two stars.	For every two stars there are five triangles.

Focus 11

Vocabulary

multiple, add, subtract, difference, sum, total, equals

Resources

RS11 TA for each child

ACTIVITY

Individuals or pairs

Children work with a copy of RS11 TA each. In each section, they use the numbers above the table to make as many additions and subtractions as they can which give each of the answers in the table. Each number can be used more than once.

For example:

70
$20 + 50$
$90 - 20$
$100 - 30$
$40 + 30$

What's five add two? How does that help you here?

What do you double to get 16? What's half of 12? How does that help?

How do you know you've done them all? Have you used every number?

Other things to do

- Make the activity into a game for pairs. Use a timer and, after five minutes, ask children to compare answers and check that each other's are correct. The child with the most correct calculations is the winner.

- Play the game as above, then take five minutes to find more calculations and score further points.

ABOUT THE MATHS

Calculations involving multiples of 10 (such as 30, 50, 90), of 100 (such as 200, 500, 800) and of 1000 (such as 3000, 4000, 7000) are much easier when children use what they know about small numbers.

If they know that:

$4 + 5 = 9$, they can work out

$40 + 50 = 90$ and $400 + 500 = 900$ and $4000 + 5000 = 9000$

It is important that children know their number bonds to 10 thoroughly.

RS11 TA

Use these numbers.
Add or subtract them to make the answers in the table.
Do as many as you can.

20, 30, 40, 50, 60, 70, 80, 90, 100, 110, 120, 130

70	160	180

Use these numbers.
Add or subtract them to make the answers in the table.
Do as many as you can.

200, 300, 400, 500, 600, 700, 800, 900, 1000, 1100, 1200, 1300

1200	600	1900

Focus 12

Doubling two-digit numbers

Vocabulary

double, halve, multiple of 10, multiple of 100

Resources

RS12 TA for each pair

Set of 20–100 number cards for each pair

Linking cubes

ACTIVITY

Pairs

Each pair has a copy of RS12 TA and linking cubes if needed. Children shuffle the number cards and place them on the table, face down. After each turn, children swap roles. Child A takes a card and records the number in secret. They double the number and record their answer. They then tell Child B their answer, and Child B says what number was on the card. If they are correct, the pair scores a point; if not, both children look at the original card and both players' answers to work out where a mistake has been made. No points are scored in this situation.

How many different ways can we think of doubling 39?

Which method do you find easiest?

Can you explain to your partner how to double 56?

Other things to do

- Roll two dice and put the numbers together to make a two-digit number. Use a calculator to double the number ($\times$ 2), but don't show the answer. Ask a child to tell you what the display shows. Correct answers win the child a counter; interruptions by someone when it isn't their turn lose the child a counter.

- Write down a two-digit number in secret. Use a calculator to double it ($\times$ 2) and show the answer. Ask a child to tell you what number you doubled.

ABOUT THE MATHS

Children may have various ways of doubling numbers, but the one they are likely to use most often is called partitioning: breaking the number down into tens and units.

Double 47?

$47 = 40 + 7$

Double 40 is 80.   **Double 7 is 14.**

$80 + 14 = 94$

So double 47 is 94.

RS12 TA

Number on card Hide this from your partner!	Double it, then tell your partner your answer.	Partner's guess at the card number	Points Correct guess? Score a point!
		Total score:	

Focus 13

Vocabulary

multiply, divide, multiple

Resources

RS13 TA for each child
Counters or linking cubes

ACTIVITY

Individuals, then pairs

Each child has a copy of RS13 TA. They fill in the facts for the 2× and 3× tables, using counters or linking cubes if necessary, then use these to work out the facts for the 4×, 6×, 8× and 9× tables.

When they have finished, children check their work, then swap sheets with a partner and check their work, too. If they think they have found any errors, both children work together to find the correct answer.

Can you explain how doubling helps to work out the 4 × and the 8 × tables?

What is double four fours the same as?

Can you show us with counters or cubes how six fives is double three fives?

Other things to do

- Look for patterns in the tables. For example, the 2×, 4× and 8× table have answers that are even. The units digits in the 6× table have a repeating pattern of 6, 2, 8, 4, 0.

- Show children a way of checking answers in the 9× table. The digits all add up to 9.

  9 × 2 = 18 (1 and 8 makes 9.)

  9 × 5 = 45 (4 and 5 makes 9.)

ABOUT THE MATHS

Double the facts in the 2x table to find the facts in the 4x table, then double again to get the facts in the 8x table.

2 × 3 = 6	4 × 3 = 12	8 × 3 = 24
2 × 7 = 14	4 × 7 = 28	8 × 7 = 56

Double the facts in the 3x table to find the facts in the 6x table. To get the facts in the 9x table, they need to multiply facts in the 3x table by 3.

3 × 4 = 12	6 × 4 = 24	9 × 4 = 36 (12 × 3)
3 × 8 = 24	6 × 8 = 48	9 × 8 = 72 (24 × 3)

$2 \times 1 =$	$4 \times 1 =$	$8 \times 1 =$
$2 \times 2 =$	$4 \times 2 =$	$8 \times 2 =$
$2 \times 3 =$	$4 \times 3 =$	$8 \times 3 =$
$2 \times 4 =$	$4 \times 4 =$	$8 \times 4 =$
$2 \times 5 =$	$4 \times 5 =$	$8 \times 5 =$
$2 \times 6 =$	$4 \times 6 =$	$8 \times 6 =$
$2 \times 7 =$	$4 \times 7 =$	$8 \times 7 =$
$2 \times 8 =$	$4 \times 8 =$	$8 \times 8 =$
$2 \times 9 =$	$4 \times 9 =$	$8 \times 9 =$
$2 \times 10 =$	$4 \times 10 =$	$8 \times 10 =$

$3 \times 1 =$	$6 \times 1 =$	$9 \times 1 =$
$3 \times 2 =$	$6 \times 2 =$	$9 \times 2 =$
$3 \times 3 =$	$6 \times 3 =$	$9 \times 3 =$
$3 \times 4 =$	$6 \times 4 =$	$9 \times 4 =$
$3 \times 5 =$	$6 \times 5 =$	$9 \times 5 =$
$3 \times 6 =$	$6 \times 6 =$	$9 \times 6 =$
$3 \times 7 =$	$6 \times 7 =$	$9 \times 7 =$
$3 \times 8 =$	$6 \times 8 =$	$9 \times 8 =$
$3 \times 9 =$	$6 \times 9 =$	$9 \times 9 =$
$3 \times 10 =$	$6 \times 10 =$	$9 \times 10 =$

Focus 14

Vocabulary

fraction, numerator, denominator, half, quarter, third, fifth, sixth, seventh, eighth, ninth, tenth, twelfth

Resources

RS14 TA for each child

ACTIVITY

Pairs

Pairs of children each have a copy of RS14 TA. They colour a fraction of each shape on RS14 TA. The pair swaps sheets and writes a sentence about each fraction.

$\frac{3}{6} + \frac{3}{6}$ makes 1

What is $\frac{3}{6}$ the same as?

How can you work out fractions of this shape?

Can you two explain how you did that?

Other things to do

- Children colour a shape from the worksheet, using two colours, and write an equation, using the fractions that go with it. For example, they might colour $\frac{2}{5}$ of the pentagon red and $\frac{3}{5}$ yellow and write $\frac{2}{5} + \frac{3}{5} = 1$.

- Children colour a shape from the sheet, using three colours, and write the three fractions that go with it. For example:

$\frac{1}{2}$ red

$\frac{1}{4}$ yellow

$\frac{1}{4}$ blue

$\frac{1}{2} + \frac{1}{4} + \frac{1}{4} = 1$

ABOUT THE MATHS

Children have been working on pairs of fractions that make 1. Many of the shapes can be divided in half, leading to the simple pair: $\frac{1}{2}$ and $\frac{1}{2}$. Many of the shapes can be divided in several ways. Encourage children to find other pairs. The whole list of possible pairs is as follows:

$$\frac{1}{3} + \frac{2}{3}$$

$$\frac{1}{4} + \frac{3}{4}$$

$$\frac{1}{5} + \frac{4}{5} \qquad \frac{2}{5} + \frac{3}{5}$$

$$\frac{1}{6} + \frac{5}{6} \qquad \frac{2}{6} + \frac{4}{6} \qquad \frac{3}{6} + \frac{3}{6}$$

$$\frac{1}{10} + \frac{9}{10} \qquad \frac{2}{10} + \frac{8}{10} \qquad \frac{3}{10} + \frac{7}{10} \qquad \frac{4}{10} + \frac{6}{10} \qquad \frac{5}{10} + \frac{5}{10}$$

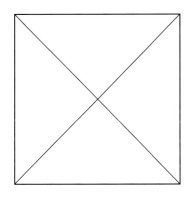

_____

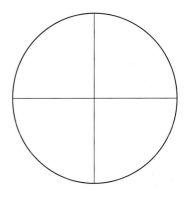

_____

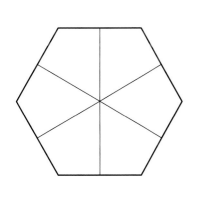

_____

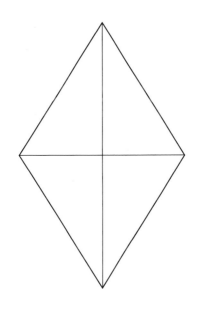

_____

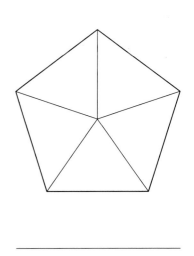

_____

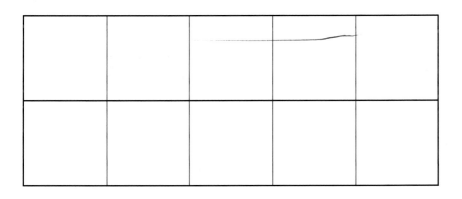

_____

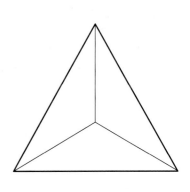

_____

Focus 15

Adding and subtracting two-digit numbers

Vocabulary
add, subtract, total, difference

Resources
RS15 TA

Two 0–9 dice for each pair

Calculators

ACTIVITY

Pairs

Each child rolls a 0–9 dice four times and records their numbers on RS15 TA. They use the numbers to create an addition calculation and then use the same numbers to create a subtraction. They find the answers to both calculations mentally.

They show their work to their partner who checks their answers with a calculator. Assuming the answers are correct, the child with the largest answer to the addition scores a point and the child with the smallest answer to the subtraction scores a point. Repeat 10 times. The child with the largest score is the winner.

Is there another way of doing that calculation? And another?

What other calculations can you do using those same dice numbers?

How can you arrange those dice numbers to make the easiest calculations? And the hardest? Why is it harder?

Other things to do

- Children use a 1–6 dice instead of a 0–9 dice. This will give a narrower range of numbers to work with, which children should find easier.

- Children roll the dice five times and choose four of the numbers to work with.

For example:

Choose the largest digits for a big total:

99 + 43 = 142

ABOUT THE MATHS

Help children look for short cuts to adding and subtracting. For example, to do 39 + 26, it is easy to do

$$40 + 26 = 66 \quad \text{then just take off 1}$$

$$39 + 26 = 65$$

Encourage children to tell you and the whole group any short cuts they can use.

Numbers	Addition	Subtraction	Score
☐ ☐ ☐ ☐	☐☐ + ☐☐ = ◯	☐☐ − ☐☐ = ◯	
☐ ☐ ☐ ☐	☐☐ + ☐☐ = ◯	☐☐ − ☐☐ = ◯	
☐ ☐ ☐ ☐	☐☐ + ☐☐ = ◯	☐☐ − ☐☐ = ◯	
☐ ☐ ☐ ☐	☐☐ + ☐☐ = ◯	☐☐ − ☐☐ = ◯	
☐ ☐ ☐ ☐	☐☐ + ☐☐ = ◯	☐☐ − ☐☐ = ◯	
☐ ☐ ☐ ☐	☐☐ + ☐☐ = ◯	☐☐ − ☐☐ = ◯	
☐ ☐ ☐ ☐	☐☐ + ☐☐ = ◯	☐☐ − ☐☐ = ◯	
☐ ☐ ☐ ☐	☐☐ + ☐☐ = ◯	☐☐ − ☐☐ = ◯	
☐ ☐ ☐ ☐	☐☐ + ☐☐ = ◯	☐☐ − ☐☐ = ◯	
☐ ☐ ☐ ☐	☐☐ + ☐☐ = ◯	☐☐ − ☐☐ = ◯	

Total score

Focus 16

Adding and subtracting
two- and three-digit numbers

Vocabulary

add, sum, total, equals, take away, subtract, difference, method

Resources

RS16 TA for each child

0–9 dice for each pair

ACTIVITY

Pairs

Each child has a copy of the RS16 TA. The pair takes turns to roll the dice five times and use the numbers in any order to make a two- and a three-digit number. They write the two numbers in the appropriate boxes on their copy of the worksheet.

Each child then adds the two numbers and writes down the answer. They score one point for each of the digits 1, 2 or 3 that they have in their answer.

Round 1			
1st number	1 3 1		
2nd number	6 2		
Total	1 9 3	Score	2

The overall winner is the child who scores most points over 6 rounds.

What are all the different ways you can arrange those dice numbers to make a two-digit number and a three-digit number?

Will any of these numbers add together to give you a 2 somewhere in the answer? What number could give you 2?

What two numbers add together to make 13? What will you do about the 10 in 13?

Other things to do

- Children roll the dice six times to make two three-digit numbers.

- Score points for 1, 2, 3 and also 4 in the answer: 1 point for a 1, 2 points for a 2, 3 points for a 3 and 4 points for a 4.

ABOUT THE MATHS

Children may be able to add two numbers mentally. Or they may prefer to use a method such as this. These children will need to work out their totals on a separate sheet of paper.

$$
\begin{array}{r}
232 \\
+ \ 29 \\
\hline
200 \\
50 \\
11 \\
\hline
261 \\
\end{array}
$$

38 | Mathematics Accomplished: Y4 Booster Teaching assistant's book

RS**16** TA

Round 1

				Total score
1st number				
2nd number				
Total		Score		

Round 2

				Total score
1st number				
2nd number				
Total		Score		

Round 3

				Total score
1st number				
2nd number				
Total		Score		

Round 4

				Total score
1st number				
2nd number				
Total		Score		

Round 5

				Total score
1st number				
2nd number				
Total		Score		

Round 6

				Total score
1st number				
2nd number				
Total		Score		

Focus 17

Vocabulary

one thousand, place, digit, place value, ten times, one hundred times

Resources

RS17 TA for each pair
Calculators

ACTIVITY

Pairs

Children key the A number into the calculator, then change the display from this number to the B number by multiplying or dividing by 10 or 100.

Children take turns to be the Operator or Instructor. The Operator only presses a key if told to do so by the Instructor. Encourage children to try and change the number in just one step.

For example:

56 × 100 = 5600

not 56 × 10 = 560 then 560 × 10 = 5600

What is your starting number? And your end number? Is that a larger or a smaller number?

How do you divide with the calculator? What keys will you press?

How can you change the answer back to the number you started with?

Other things to do

- Children draw up their own list of A and B numbers and challenge a friend to get from one to the other by multiplying or dividing by 10 or 100.

- Children key in a number (not more than 1000), then multiply or divide it by 10 or 100. They say what they have done, but do not show the answer. Their partner must say what the calculator now shows.

ABOUT THE MATHS

Multiplying and dividing by 10 and 100 is straightforward, as long as children remember the rules:

× 10 **Move the number one place to the left and put a zero in the units place.**

T U   H T U
4 5 × 10 = 4 5 0

× 100 **Move the number two places to the left and put a zero in the tens and units place.**

T U   T H T U
4 5 × 100 = 4 5 0 0

The reverse holds true for dividing by 10 and 100: take off one or two zeros and move the number to the right.

Number A	Number B
56	5600
270	27
36 000	360
45 000	4500
81	810
970	97 000
67 000	670
34	3400
286	2860
874	87 400
26 500	265
61 200	6120

Play this game with your partner.

Take turns to be the Operator and the Instructor.

Operator, listen carefully to your partner.
Only press what they tell you to.

Instructor, now tell them what keys to press.
You want the calculator to show the B number.

Focus 18

Multiplying two-digit number by a one-digit number

Vocabulary

multiply, times, product, equals, method

Resources

RS18 TA for each group
Counters

ACTIVITY

Groups of four

Each group of four children works with a copy of RS18 TA and some coloured counters.

The two pairs take turns to choose a number from the cloud and a number from the heart. They say them aloud first and then find their product, using pencil and paper. If their answer appears on their grid, they place a counter on that number. The first pair to complete one of their columns (that is, get five counters in a vertical line) is the winner.

How are you going to work out 7×38?

What jottings will you make?

Can you explain to the other pair how you worked out that calculation?

Other things to do

- One pair checks the other pair's multiplication on a calculator.

- Children devise their own sheet like this, choosing numbers to put in the cloud and the heart.

ABOUT THE MATHS

There are two main methods children are likely to use to multiply their numbers, one called the grid method and the other a standard written multiplication.

Grid method:

	20	6
× 7	140	42	= 182

Standard written multiplication:

$$\begin{array}{r} 26 \\ \times\,7 \\ \hline \end{array}$$

$$\begin{array}{rr} 20 \times 7 = & 140 \\ 6 \times 7 = & 42 \\ \hline & 182 \end{array}$$

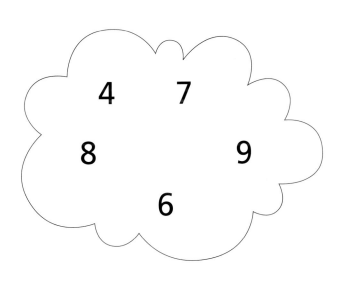

Team A		
108	416	152
208	308	312
408	258	162
616	364	387
301	189	342

Team B		
172	344	468
272	216	228
539	304	462
243	476	266
612	544	693

Focus 19

Vocabulary

divide, divisible, remainder, method

Resources

RS19 TA for each pair

0–9 digit cards

ACTIVITY

Pairs

Pairs of children work with a copy of RS19 TA and a set of digit cards. They take turns to shuffle the cards and pick three to place on the table, face up. Each child uses these three digits to make a division calculation where a two-digit number is divided by a one-digit number. The aim is to choose the calculation that gives the lowest remainder.

The child who picked the cards goes first and writes their calculation on the sheet. Their partner must use the same digits, but cannot write the same calculation. The pair finds and agrees the answers to the calculations and records the remainders on the sheet. After five rounds, children add up the remainders. The child with the lowest total is the winner.

How will you arrange your cards differently to make another calculation?

Can you explain your method to me?

Has anyone used a different method?

Other things to do

- Use 1–6 digit cards or a 1–6 dice to keep the numbers small and simple.

- Check divisions on a calculator. For example, to check $52 \div 3 = 17$ r 1, multiply the answer, 17, by 3 and add on the remainder 1. If you get back to the starting number, 52, the division was correct.

$$\boxed{17} \times \boxed{3} + \boxed{1} = 52$$

ABOUT THE MATHS

Children may be able to use informal or mental methods for their divisions. The written method they have learnt with the teacher involves taking off several 'chunks' at a time. You can ask children to show you the method and explain how it works: this would give them valuable experience in explanation.

$$97 \div 6$$

```
   6 | 97
     − 60        10 × 6
       37
     − 30         5 × 6
        7
      − 6         1 × 6
        1        16 × 6
```

The answer is 16 remainder 1.

Cards	Name _____		Name _____	
	Calculation	Remainder	Calculation	Remainder
	Total		Total	

Focus 20

Vocabulary

fraction, quarter, half, three-quarters, fifth, sixth, seventh, eighth, ninth

Resources

Set of cards cut from RS20 TA for each pair
Multiplication grids

ACTIVITY

Pairs

Children shuffle the cards and spread them out on the table, face up. They take turns to pick a card until they each have five cards. Each child works out the answers for their cards and finds the total of their answers. They then swap their work with their partner to check.

Once the pair has agreed that each other's answers are correct, the player with the higher total is the winner.

Encourage children to look carefully at the cards as they select them and try to pick cards that will give them the largest answers. Children play the game again and see if they make better decisions.

Which will give you a larger answer, half of 24 or half of 50?

Do you think one eighth of 80 is larger or smaller than five eighths of 40? Why?

Can you explain how you worked out five ninths of 36?

Other things to do

- Pick two cards and ask children to say which amount they would prefer to win as prize money if the answer referred to pound coins.

- Help children use a multiplication grid to work out divisions they don't know and to check their calculations with a calculator.

ABOUT THE MATHS

Finding a fraction of a number is simple when the numerator (the top number of the fraction) is 1. Divide the number you want to find the fraction of by the denominator (the bottom number of the fraction).

$\frac{1}{2}$ of 24? $24 \div 2$ is 12, so $\frac{1}{2}$ of 24 is 12.

$\frac{1}{5}$ of 45? $45 \div 5$ is 9, so $\frac{1}{5}$ of 45 is 9.

When the numerator is not 1, you need to make an extra step. To find two sixths, you find one sixth and multiply the answer by two.

$\frac{2}{6}$ of 12? $12 \div 6$ is 2, so $\frac{1}{6}$ of 12 is 2.

2×2 is 4, so $\frac{2}{6}$ of 12 is 4.

✂

$\frac{1}{5}$ of 60	$\frac{1}{3}$ of 30	$\frac{5}{6}$ of 24	$\frac{3}{7}$ of 49
$\frac{2}{5}$ of 25	$\frac{1}{2}$ of 24	$\frac{1}{2}$ of 50	$\frac{2}{7}$ of 28
$\frac{4}{9}$ of 27	$\frac{1}{8}$ of 80	$\frac{5}{8}$ of 40	$\frac{2}{6}$ of 12
$\frac{4}{6}$ of 42	$\frac{2}{3}$ of 15	$\frac{5}{9}$ of 36	$\frac{5}{7}$ of 35
$\frac{3}{8}$ of 48	$\frac{4}{6}$ of 36	$\frac{2}{9}$ of 18	$\frac{1}{2}$ of 60

Focus 21

Using a calculator

Vocabulary

calculator, display, key, enter, entry, clear, answer, pound, pence

Resources

RS21 TA for each child
Calculators

ACTIVITY

Individuals, then pairs

Each child has their own copy of RS21 TA. They work out the calculations, using a calculator where they think this would be helpful, and answer the question. They then compare answers with another child and check whether they have the same answers to their calculations. If not, ask them to go over their calculations and try to find the correct answer.

How can you check that you've done that calculation right?

Can you estimate, very roughly, what sort of number the answer will be?

Why do you think that answer will be larger than that one?

Other things to do

- Children write their own 'Would you rather' for another child to do.

- Children write down a calculation, then do it on the calculator, making a deliberate error. Their partner looks at the calculation and the answer in the display and tries to work out what error they made.

ABOUT THE MATHS

Children need to develop confidence in working with calculators, and this can only come with experience. Not every key they press results in a visible change in the display, and this can be confusing. For example, they press 245. Then they press the $\boxed{-}$ key and nothing changes. Then they press 45 and the 245 disappears, to be replaced by 45. Finally they press $\boxed{=}$ and a new number appears, the answer.

$$\boxed{200}$$

All this means children may forget what keys they have pressed; if this seems to happen, ask them to write down the keys before they press them and to check that the answer looks sensible when it appears in the display.

What would you rather win, 234 lots of £16 or 187 lots of £36?

Calculations	Answer

Would you rather be chased by $167 + 58 + 598$ bees or $983 - 279$ bees?

Calculations	Answer

Would you rather have 530×12 grapes or $1035 \div 9$ cherries?

Calculations	Answer

Would you rather eat $3456 - 2179$ slugs or $345 + 467 + 478$ toads?

Calculations	Answer

Focus 22

Classifying and drawing polygons

Vocabulary

polygon, rectangle, square, triangle, equilateral triangle, isosceles triangle, pentagon, hexagon, quadrilateral, octagon, regular, irregular, right angle, line of symmetry, sides, vertex, vertices

Resources

Shapes property cards cut from RS22 TA

Shapes (picture cards or plastic shapes)

Large sheet of paper

Mirror (optional)

ACTIVITY

Whole group

Draw a line down the middle of the large sheet of paper and write 'Yes' and 'No' at the top of the different sides. Choose a shapes property card and place it by the paper. Spread out the shapes on the table (face down if you are using cards). Children take turns to pick a shape and place it in the appropriate place on the paper. Make sure everyone in the group agrees with where the shape goes.

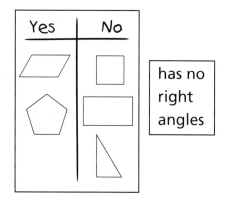

When all the shapes are in the correct place, start again with another property card.

In what way are these shapes like each other? Can you find another one that has that same property?

Can you show us how to trace the line of symmetry in that shape? Can anyone find another with a line of symmetry?

What makes this shape the odd one out?

Other things to do

- Share out any shapes between the children. Take a property card and read it out. Any child with a shape that matches that description wins a counter (just one counter even if they have two shapes that fit).

- Put shapes into a feely bag. Children touch, describe and name the shape before they pull it out of the bag.

ABOUT THE MATHS

Regular polygons have all their sides **and** all angles equal.

Examples are a square or a pentagon like this:

Irregular polygons do not have all their sides and angles equal.

Examples are a rectangle or a pentagon like this:

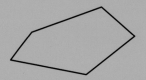

Allow yourself and the children to take your time looking at each shape and deciding whether it matches the description on your card: count the sides, identify and count the right angles and, if necessary, check for symmetry with a mirror.

is an irregular polygon	is a regular polygon	has no lines of symmetry
has at least one line of symmetry	has at least one right angle	has no equal sides
has no right angles	has an even number of sides	has an odd number of sides
has two or more equal sides	has at least two equal angles	has no equal angles

Focus 23

Visualising 3D solids

ACTIVITY

Whole group

Children work with a copy of RS23 TA. They make each shape with plastic connecting shapes, then open out their shapes to form nets. Children then draw a sketch of their net on the worksheet.

Is there another way you can open that shape up and fold it flat?

Does it matter where you put that square? Will it still fold up to make a cube?

Is there anywhere else you could join up that triangle and still make a tetrahedron?

Other things to do

- Cut out (or photocopy and cut up) the completed sheets. Give children one of the sketched nets and recreate the original shape from plastic connecting shapes.

- Children make other shapes from plastic connecting shapes and draw the shape and its net.

ABOUT THE MATHS

The net of a hollow 3D shape is the shape it opens out into. For example, a cube has several nets, including these two:

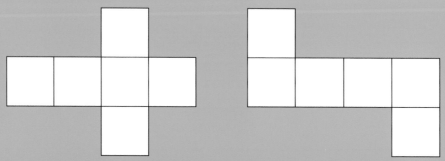

The 3D shapes children make here will all have several possible nets. Encourage children to prove by folding that their net works.

Shape	Net
Cuboid	
Triangular prism	
Square-based pyramid	
Cube	
Tetrahedron	

Focus 24

Vocabulary

grid, row, column, horizontal, vertical, north, south, east, west

Resources

RS24 TA for each child
Coloured pencils

ACTIVITY

Pairs

Each child works with a grid from RS24 TA. Both children draw a pattern on their grid by colouring in, for example, 10 squares with coloured pencils. The squares must be spread out around the grid.

They do this out of sight of their partner. Still keeping their grid hidden, they then take it in turns to give directions to their partner, giving the position of a starting square and its colour and directing their partner to the rest of the squares to colour, using compass directions. For example, "Start at (B, 4). Colour it blue. Move two squares north and one square east and colour it yellow."

After the squares have been coloured in, children show each other their patterns to see if they are the same.

Can you describe how to get from this yellow square to this blue one?

How do you know whether the green square is north or south of the red square?

If I start at J10 and go to J4, which direction did I go in?

Other things to do

- One child puts 12 counters or beans on squares on the grid and secretly puts a scrap of paper under one of them. Their partner starts at square A1 and moves as instructed to the square with the hidden scrap of paper.

- Draw a thick 'mirror line' on top of the line between E and F. One child colours 10 squares on the left-hand side, then instructs their partner which to colour on the other side – these must be the squares that are reflections of the squares they coloured. The partner only colours the squares they are told to, so the first child must take responsibility for giving correct instructions.

ABOUT THE MATHS

Children should always say the horizontal 'label' first and the vertical one second (in the house and up the stairs). When they write them, they should put both in brackets with a comma between: for example, (B, 3), not (3, B).

Expect children to use the four compass directions, as described above: for example, "Start at (B, 4). Colour it blue. Move two squares north and one square east and colour it yellow."

Children do not need to use the other directions such as north-east and south-west.

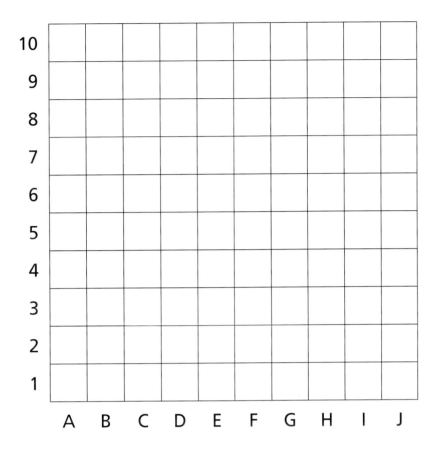

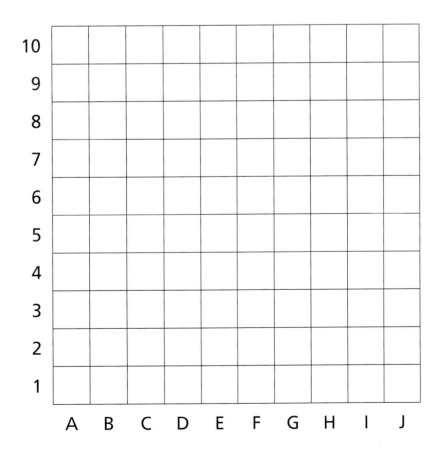

Focus 25

Vocabulary

angle, right angle, degree, greater than, less than, turn

Resources

RS25 TA for each child

ACTIVITY

Pairs

Pairs share cards cut from RS25 TA and match each picture card with a description card.

For example:

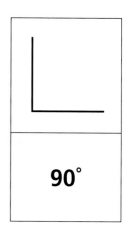

90°

Child A shuts their eyes while Child B swaps around two cards. Child A opens their eyes and spots what has been changed. But they must not touch the cards; instead, they say what is wrong and instruct their partner how to replace the cards.

Can you show us why that angle is less than a right angle?

How can you show that a straight line is the same as two right angles?

Can you draw another angle that is more than 90 degrees?

Other things to do

- Children draw another two angle cards to add to their set and write their matching description cards.

- Play Pelmanism: a pair of children spreads a set of the cards face down on the table. They take turns to turn two cards face up. If the cards match, that child keeps both cards. If the cards do not match, children return them to their original place on the table, face down.

ABOUT THE MATHS

Children need to know that:

- a right angle is the same as 90°

- a straight line is the same as 180°

If they need help matching the cards, help them turn them round so that the angles are facing the same way. Then it will be easier to spot which is larger. They can make their own right-angle measure by cutting off the corner of a sheet of paper and fitting that onto the angles.

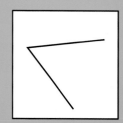 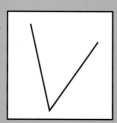

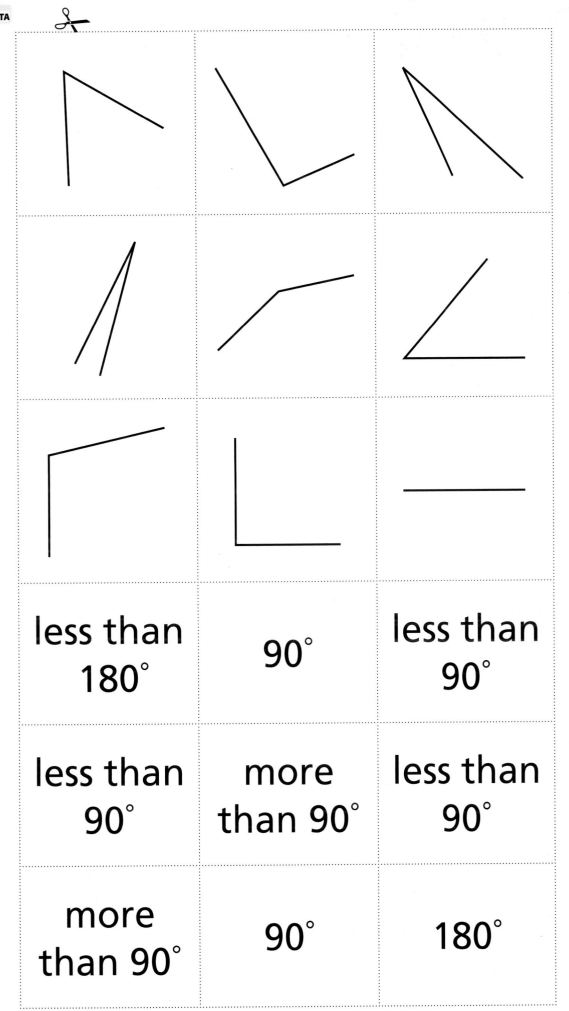

less than 180°	90°	less than 90°
less than 90°	more than 90°	less than 90°
more than 90°	90°	180°

Focus 26

Vocabulary

measure, unit, measuring scale, division, marker, weight, length, kilogram, gram, centimetre, millimetre, litre, centilitre, scales, estimate, heavier, lighter

Resources

RS26 TA for each pair

Different lengths of string for each pair (less than 30 cm)

Rulers

ACTIVITY

Pairs

Pairs of children take each piece of string in turn. Both children estimate the length of the string and record their estimate. Children then measure the string and agree on its actual length. If a child's estimate was within a centimetre of the correct length, they score 20 points. If they were within 5 cm, they score 10 points, and if they were within 10 cm, they score 5 points.

Children then choose the next piece of string to estimate.

The child with the highest score at the end is the winner.

Have you got better at estimating now that you have measured a few?

How long do you think your little finger is?

Is anyone using a pencil between 10 and 15 cm long?

Other things to do

- One child says a length between 2 and 30 cm. Another child cuts a piece of string which they estimate is that length.

- You could provide tape measures and do the activity with longer pieces of string up to 1 metre.

String	Estimated length		Actual length
	Name Jack	Name Lauren	
1	12.5 cm	14 cm	11 cm 4 mm

ABOUT THE MATHS

Expect children to **estimate** in whole centimetres (for example, 11 cm), but to **measure** in centimetres and millimetres (for example, 11 cm 3 mm).

Remind children if necessary to measure from the 0 on the ruler, not from the beginning of the ruler (unless the ruler starts at 0, which many don't). They should make sure the string is straight but not stretch it.

Score

Name	Name										

Total

Estimated length

String	Name	Name	Actual length
1			
2			
3			
4			
5			
6			
7			
8			
9			
10			

Focus 27

Vocabulary

perimeter, area, surface, covers, length, width, distance

Resources

RS27 TA for each pair
Squared paper (1 cm)

ACTIVITY

Pairs

Pairs of children shuffle the cards cut from RS27 TA and place them in a pile, face down. They turn over the top card. Each child draws a shape on cm squared paper that matches the criteria on the card. They then compare their shapes and discuss whether they are correct or not. When both children are happy that each shape drawn is correct, they select another card.

Can you give us all a definition of 'perimeter' and 'area'? Can you show us an example?

How are you going to count these half squares?

How many different shapes can you draw with an area of 6 square cm?

Other things to do

- One child says an area between 2 cm² and 30 cm². Another child draws a shape which is that area.

- Children cut out their shapes and put them in order of size.

ABOUT THE MATHS

Measuring an area on a centimetre square grid is fairly straightforward. But in this activity, children have to work backward – given an area, they must draw a shape to match. It is important that they understand that different shapes can have the same area.

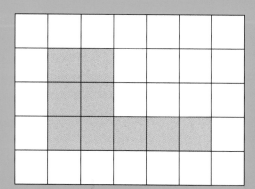

Area: 9 square centimetres or 9 cm²

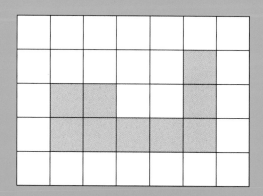

Area: 9 square centimetres or 9 cm²

Area of 24 cm^2	Perimeter of 20 cm and area of 16 cm^2
Area of 12 cm^2	Perimeter of 20 cm and area of 24 cm^2
Area of 36 cm^2	Area between 10 cm^2 and 20 cm^2
Area of 18 cm^2	Area of 6 cm^2

Focus 28

Calculating with time

Vocabulary

timetable, morning, afternoon, evening, night, hour, minute, second, am, pm

Resources

RS28 TA

Materials to create a poster

ACTIVITY

Pairs

Children devise a video/DVD viewing timetable for two hours one afternoon. The timetable should be for a complete two hours, with no gaps or overlaps.

They record the start and finish times of each in the form of a poster.

For example:

	Start	Finish
Robot wars	1:30 pm	2:15 pm

What do you think you'd like to watch after watching that for 50 minutes? Have you still got time?

How much time have you got left now?

Do you need to invent a 5-minute programme to slot in at the end?

Other things to do

- Children have a limit of 12 hours' TV viewing in a week. They decide what programmes they would pick from a weekly TV schedule.

- Show children a real timetable used in your school and work out how long the sessions are.

ABOUT THE MATHS

Children should have little difficulty reading and writing times digitally: for example, 5:55. Encourage them to use 'am' and 'pm' as well (all the afternoon sessions will, of course, be pm, as in 2:30 pm).

There is no set way for children to tackle this task, so it is a good idea to discuss it with them and let them share ideas about what to do. If they seem short of ideas, give them hints about how you yourself would tackle it.

Title	Start	Finish

Focus 29

Answering questions by collecting and organising data

Vocabulary

data, information, survey, graph, chart, table, axis, axes, label, title, bar graph

Resources

RS29 TA for each pair

ACTIVITY

Pairs

Read the passage on RS29 TA and the questions, as a whole group. Pairs of children then choose one of the questions to answer.

Is 5 letters the most common length of word?

Is 'a' the most common vowel in the passage? (The five vowels are a, e, i, o and u.)

They create a table and collect the information they need to answer the questions. They then display their findings in a block graph and write a statement in answer to the question.

What do you think is the most common consonant in the passage? And what do your findings show?

Which letters of the alphabet don't appear in this passage? How many of these are there?

What's the second most common vowel?

Other things to do

- Choose your own text for children to work with or let them choose their own. About 30 to 40 words is plenty.

- Children write two true statements about their graph and two false ones; they then swap graphs with another pair who try to spot which are the true and which are the false ones.

ABOUT THE MATHS

To answer the question 'Is 5 letters the most common length of word?', children can do a tally of words of different lengths and record them in a table like this:

1 letter	I
2 letters	卌
3 letters	卌 卌 II
and so on	

They then will need to display this information as a bar graph, using the grid on RS29 TA as a base.

To answer the question "Is 'a' the most common vowel in the passage?", children will need to count every vowel, record them in a table and display the information as a block graph, as above.

A bar graph is sometimes known as a bar chart, and the numbering is written on the axis divisions.

"It was a hot, even sultry day. Girish sat on the terrace, sipping lemonade and wondering when the children would be home from school. He did not see or hear the tiger crouching in the undergrowth."

Questions

Is 5 letters the most common length of word?

Is 'a' the most common vowel in the passage?

Title of graph _____

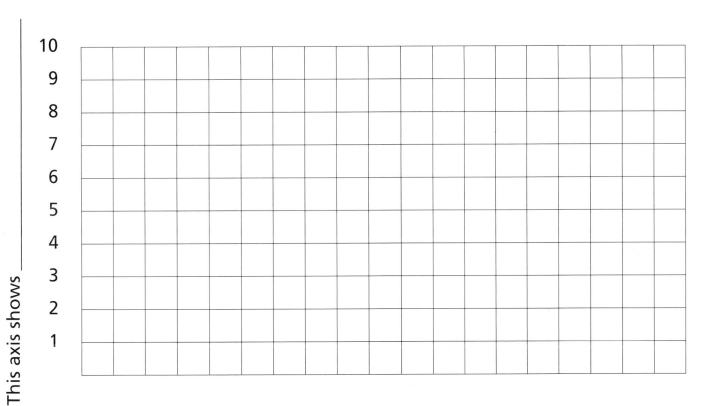

This axis shows _____

Focus 30

Vocabulary

scale, axis, interval, step, size, interpret

Resources

RS30 TA for each pair

ACTIVITY

Pairs

Children look at the top graph, which is correct. They then alter the bottom graph so that it shows the same data as the top one.

What is different about the second chart? Have a careful look.

How many children altogether took part in this survey?

What other questions could we ask about the graph?

Other things to do

- Children add on another column to each chart, for a vegetable of their choice. They will need to invent the number of children who voted for it and make sure they show the same number on each chart.

- Do a survey among the group and see if they have similar tastes.

ABOUT THE MATHS

The top graph shows the following data:

Carrots favourite	**20 children**
Peas favourite	**50 children**
Potatoes favourite	**30 children**
Broccoli favourite	**30 children**
Cabbage favourite	**20 children**

All the bars on the bottom graph are too short, and children will need to lengthen them to the correct division. But the graph will not look like the top one, as the numbers on the vertical axis are different. For example, the 'peas' column in the bottom graph needs only come up one more division, to 50, and won't go all the way to the top.

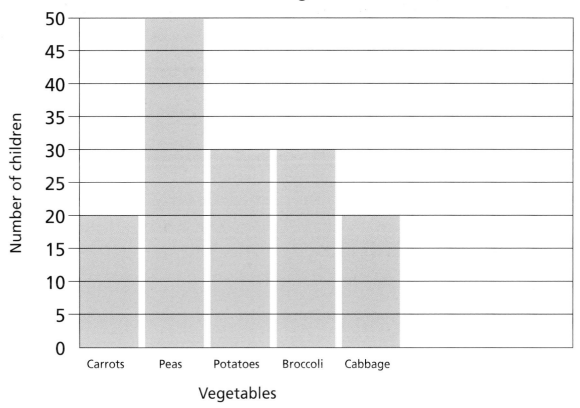

Children's favourite vegetables

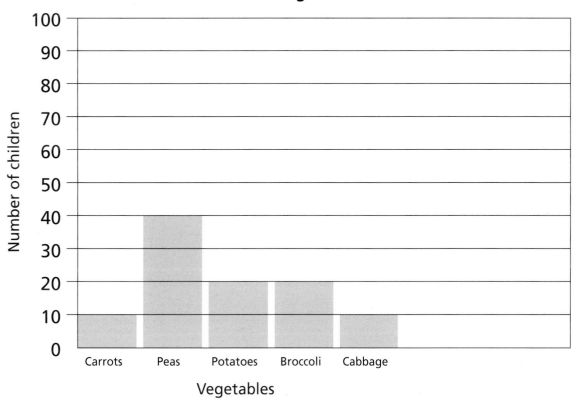

Children's favourite vegetables

These two graphs show data collected by two children
about favourite vegetables in their school.
The top graph is correct, but the bottom one is not finished.
Add to the bottom graph so it shows the same data as the top one.

×	1	2	3	4	5	6	7	8	9	10
1	1	2	3	4	5	6	7	8	9	10
2	2	4	6	8	10	12	14	16	18	20
3	3	6	9	12	15	18	21	24	27	30
4	4	8	12	16	20	24	28	32	36	40
5	5	10	15	20	25	30	35	40	45	50
6	6	12	18	24	30	36	42	48	54	60
7	7	14	21	28	35	42	49	56	63	70
8	8	16	24	32	40	48	56	64	72	80
9	9	18	27	36	45	54	63	72	81	90
10	10	20	30	40	50	60	70	80	90	100

1	2	3	4	5	6	7	8	9	10
11	12	13	14	15	16	17	18	19	20
21	22	23	24	25	26	27	28	29	30
31	32	33	34	35	36	37	38	39	40
41	42	43	44	45	46	47	48	49	50
51	52	53	54	55	56	57	58	59	60
61	62	63	64	65	66	67	68	69	70
71	72	73	74	75	76	77	78	79	80
81	82	83	84	85	86	87	88	89	90
91	92	93	94	95	96	97	98	99	100

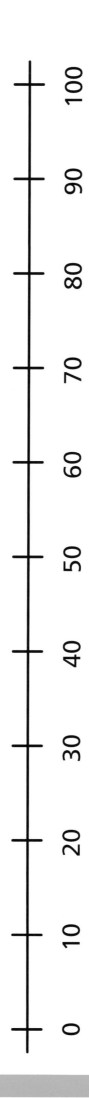

✂

−20	−19	−18	−17	−16	−15
−14	−13	−12	−11	−10	−9
−8	−7	−6	−5	−4	−3
−2	−1	0	1	2	3
4	5	6	7	8	9
10	11	12	13	14	15
16	17	18	19	20	

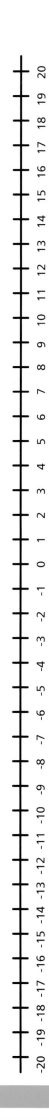

1000	2000	3000	4000	5000	6000	7000	8000	9000
100	200	300	400	500	600	700	800	900
10	20	30	40	50	60	70	80	90
1	2	3	4	5	6	7	8	9
0.1	0.2	0.3	0.4	0.5	0.6	0.7	0.8	0.9
0.01	0.02	0.03	0.04	0.05	0.06	0.07	0.08	0.09

Hundreds	Tens	Units ●	tenths	hundredths

0	1
2	3
4	5
6	7
8	9

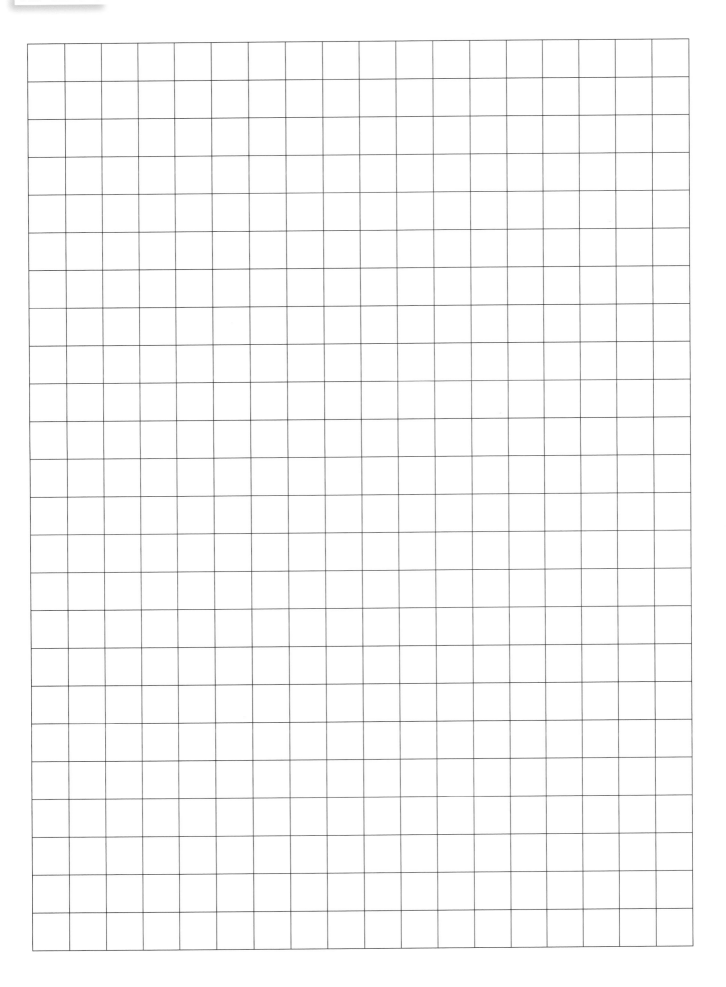

RS **Extra** TA

Visit us at www.beam.co.uk

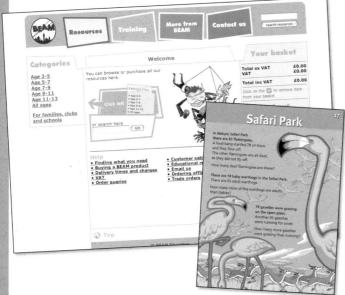

Browse for BEAM resources
You can search for resources, take a look at sample pages and order online.

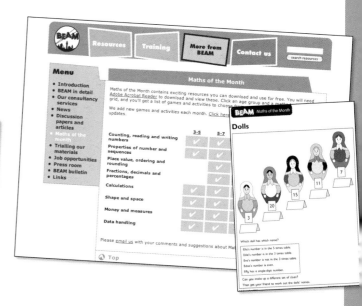

Try out some of our free activity sheets
You can download free games and activities for 3- to 13-year olds to use in your classroom or for homework.

Dip into some interesting research
You'll find some interesting research papers and informative articles on maths education to download.

Take a look at our professional development
You can choose from our extensive range of courses, or find out more about the BEAM Conference.

Sign up for the BEAM Bulletin
Our free monthly email newsletter will give you news on:

- Maths of the Month – a regular reminder, so you know when we've added new free downloadable games and activities

- New publications – a chance to find out more about our latest resources, including new titles not in the catalogue

- Courses and conferences – keep up to date with our PD programme, including new courses that we organise during the year

  To receive the BEAM Bulletin, email your name and email address to news@beam.co.uk